my **little Treasury**

Mother Goose

pi kids® publications international, ltd.

Contents

Old MacDonald's Farm

The Learned Pig

My learned friend and neighbor pig,
  Odds bobs and bills, and dash my wig!
It's said that you the weather know.
  Please tell me when the wind will blow.

A Dozen Eggs

I bought a dozen new-laid eggs

From good old Farmer Dickens.

I hobbled home upon two legs

And found them full of chickens.

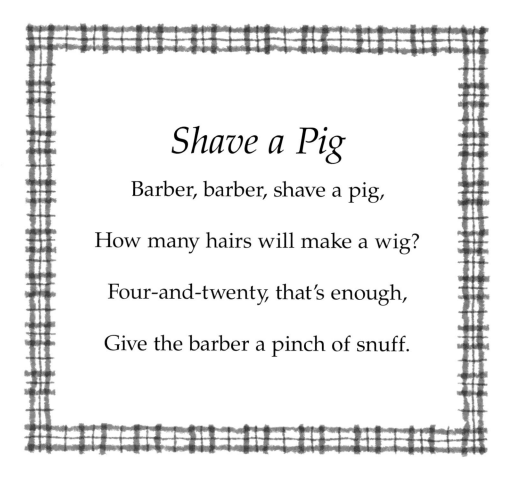

Shave a Pig

Barber, barber, shave a pig,

How many hairs will make a wig?

Four-and-twenty, that's enough,

Give the barber a pinch of snuff.

There Was a Little Pig

There was a little pig,
Who wasn't very big,
So they put him in a great big show.

While playing in the band,
He broke his little hand,
And now he can't play his old banjo.

A Horse and a Flea

A horse and a flea
    and three blind mice
Met each other
    while skating on ice.
The horse he slipped
    and fell on the flea.
The flea said, "Oops!
    There's a horse on me!"

Old MacDonald

Old MacDonald had a farm, *E-I-E-I-O.*
On his farm he had some cows, *E-I-E-I-O.*
With a moo-moo here and a moo-moo there,
Here a moo, there a moo, everywhere a moo-moo.

Old MacDonald had a farm, *E-I-E-I-O.*
On his farm he had some donkeys, *E-I-E-I-O.*
With a hee-haw here and a hee-haw there,
Here a hee, there a haw,
everywhere a hee-haw.

Old MacDonald had a farm, *E-I-E-I-O*.
On this farm he had some pigs, *E-I-E-I-O*.
With an oink-oink here and an oink-oink there,
Here an oink, there an oink,
  everywhere an oink-oink.

Old MacDonald had a farm, *E-I-E-I-O*.
On this farm he had some ducks, *E-I-E-I-O*.
With a quack-quack here and a quack-quack there,
Here a quack, there a quack,
  everywhere a quack-quack.

Old MacDonald had a farm,
  E-I-E-I-O.

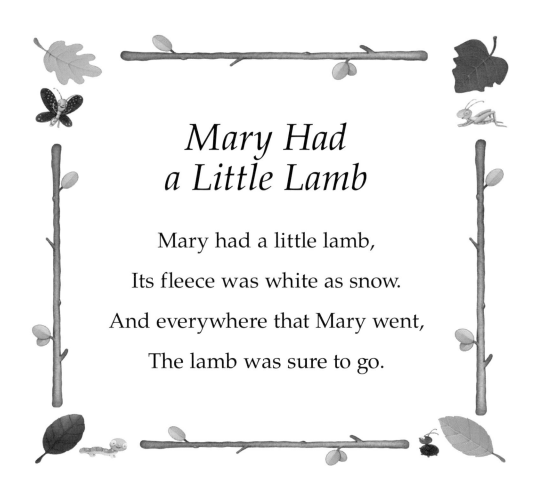

Mary Had
a Little Lamb

Mary had a little lamb,

Its fleece was white as snow.

And everywhere that Mary went,

The lamb was sure to go.

Baa, Baa, Black Sheep

Baa, baa, black sheep,
Have you any wool?
Yes, sir. Yes, sir.
Three bags full.
One for the master,
One for the dame,
And one for the little boy
Who lives down the lane.
Baa, baa, black sheep,
Have you any wool?
Yes, sir. Yes, sir.
Three bags full.

Three Blind Mice

Three blind mice, three blind mice.
See how they run, see how they run!
They all ran after the poor farmer's wife,
Who has been afraid of mice all her life.
Did you ever think you'd see such a sight,
As three blind mice that create such a fright?

Three blind mice.

Silly People Rhymes

Mary, Mary

Mary, Mary, quite contrary,
How does your garden grow?
With silver bells and cockleshells,
And pretty maids all in a row.

The House that Jack Built

This is the house that Jack built.
This is the malt that lay
In the house that Jack built.

This is the rat that ate the malt
That lay in the house that Jack built.

This is the cat that killed the rat
That ate the malt in the house that Jack built.

This is the dog that worried the cat
That killed the rat that ate the malt
That lay in the house that Jack built.

This is the cow with the crumpled horn
That tossed the dog that worried the cat
That killed the rat that ate the malt
That lay in the house that Jack built.

This is the maiden all forlorn
That milked the cow
    with the crumpled horn
That tossed the dog that worried the cat
That killed the rat that ate the malt
That lay in the house that Jack built.

This is the man all tattered and torn
That kissed the maiden all forlorn
That milked the cow with the crumpled horn
That tossed the dog that worried the cat ...

That killed the rat that ate the malt
That lay in the house that Jack built.

This is the priest all shaven and shorn
That married the man
    all tattered and torn
That kissed the maiden all forlorn
That milked the cow
    with the crumpled horn

That tossed the dog that worried the cat
That killed the rat that ate the malt
That lay in the house that Jack built.

This is the farmer sowing his corn
That kept the rooster that crowed in the morn
That waked the priest all shaven and shorn

That married the man
    all tattered and torn
That kissed the maiden all forlorn
That milked the cow
    with the crumpled horn

That tossed the dog that worried the cat
That killed the rat that ate the malt
That lay in the house that Jack built.

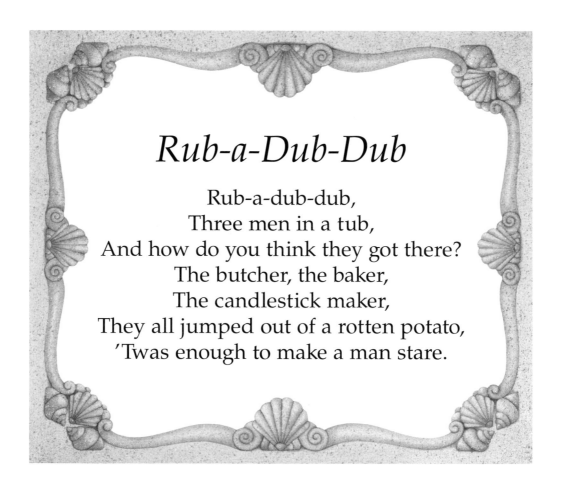

Rub-a-Dub-Dub

Rub-a-dub-dub,
Three men in a tub,
And how do you think they got there?
The butcher, the baker,
The candlestick maker,
They all jumped out of a rotten potato,
'Twas enough to make a man stare.

If Wishes Were Horses

If wishes were horses,
Beggars would ride.
If turnips were watches,
I would wear one by my side.
And if "ifs" and "ands"
Were pots and pans,
There'd be no work for tinkers!

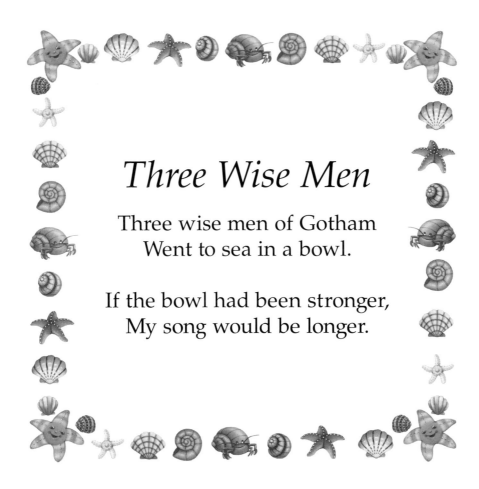

Three Wise Men

Three wise men of Gotham
Went to sea in a bowl.

If the bowl had been stronger,
My song would be longer.

Tweedle-dum and Tweedle-dee

Tweedle-dum and Tweedle-dee
Resolved to have a battle.
For Tweedle-dum said Tweedle-dee
Had spoiled his nice new rattle.

Just then flew by a monstrous crow,
As big as a tar barrel.
Which frightened both the heroes so,
They quite forgot their quarrel.

Play-Along Rhymes

Georgie Porgie

Georgie Porgie, pudding and pie,
Kissed the girls and made them cry.
When the boys came out to play,
Georgie Porgie ran away.

Here We Go Round the Mulberry Bush

Here we go round the mulberry bush,
The mulberry bush,
The mulberry bush.
Here we go round the mulberry bush,
On a cold and frosty morning.

Rain, Rain, Go Away

Rain, rain, go away,

Come again another day;

Little Johnny wants to play.

This Little Piggy

This little piggy went to market.
This little piggy stayed home.
This little piggy had roast beef.
This little piggy had none.
This little piggy cried,
"Wee-wee-wee!"
All the way home.

*Little
Boys
and
Girls*

Patience Is a Virtue

Patience is a virtue,
Virtue is a grace;
Grace is a little girl
Who wouldn't wash her face.

Little Jack Horner

Little Jack Horner
Sat in a corner
Eating his Christmas pie;

He put in his thumb,
And pulled out a plum,
And cried, "What a good boy am I!"

There Was a Little Girl

The was a little girl who had a little curl,
Right in the middle of her forehead.
And when she was good, she was very, very good,
But when she was bad, she was horrid.

She stood on her head on her little trundle bed,
With no one there to say "no."
She screamed and she squalled, she yelled and she bawled,
And drummed her little heels against the window.

Her mother heard the noise, and thought it was the toys,
Falling in the dusty attic.
She rushed up the flight, and saw she was alright,
And hugged her most emphatic.

Little Miss Muffet

Little Miss Muffet
Sat on a tuffet,
Eating her curds and whey.

There came a big spider,
Who sat down beside her
And frightened Miss Muffet away.

My Little Brother

Little brother, darling boy,
You are very dear to me!
I am happy — full of joy,
When your smiling face I see.

How I wish that you could speak,
And could know the words I say!
Pretty stories I would seek,
To amuse you every day.

Shake your rattle, here it is,
Listen to its merry noise;
And when you are tired of this,
I will bring you other toys.

My Little Sister

I have a little sister,
She is only two years old;
But to us at home who love her,
She is worth her weight in gold.

We often play together,
And I begin to find,
That to make my sister happy,
I must be very kind.

I must not taunt or tease her,
Or ever angry be
With the darling little sister
That God has given to me.

Little Polly Flinders

Little Polly Flinders,
Sat among the cinders,
Warming her pretty little toes;
Her mother came and stopped her,
For fear her lovely daughter
Would toast her pretty little nose.

Busy-Time Rhymes

To Market

To market, to market, to buy a fat pig;
    Home again, home again, jiggety-jig.
To market, to market, to buy a fat hog;
    Home again, home again, jiggety-jog.

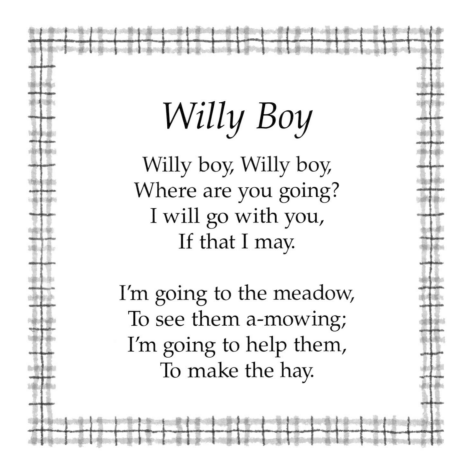

Willy Boy

Willy boy, Willy boy,
Where are you going?
I will go with you,
If that I may.

I'm going to the meadow,
To see them a-mowing;
I'm going to help them,
To make the hay.

Peter Piper

Peter Piper picked a peck
Of pickled peppers;
A peck of pickled peppers
Peter Piper picked.

If Peter Piper picked a peck
Of pickled peppers,
Where's the peck of pickled peppers
Peter Piper picked?

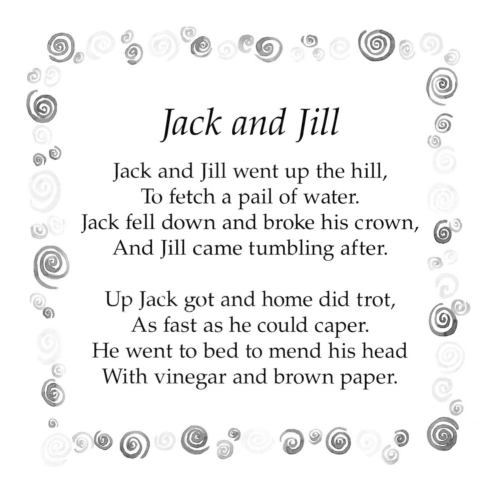

Jack and Jill

Jack and Jill went up the hill,
To fetch a pail of water.
Jack fell down and broke his crown,
And Jill came tumbling after.

Up Jack got and home did trot,
As fast as he could caper.
He went to bed to mend his head
With vinegar and brown paper.

I Love You Rhymes

Molly, My Sister

Molly, my sister, and I fell out,
And what do you think it was all about?
She loved coffee and I loved tea,
And that was the reason we couldn't agree.

Lavender Blue

Lavender blue and rosemary green,
When I am king you shall be queen.

Call up my maids at four o'clock,
Some to the wheel and some to the rock.

Some to make hay and some to shear corn,
And you and I will sing until morn.

A Fish for You

There once was a fish.
What more could you wish?
He lived in the sea.
Where else would he be?
He was caught on a line.
Whose line if not mine?
So I brought him to you.
What else should I do?

Boy and Girl

There was a little boy and a little girl
     Lived in an alley;
Says the little boy to the little girl,
     "Shall I, oh, shall I?"
Says the little girl to the little boy,
     "What shall we do?"
Says the little boy to the little girl,
     "I will kiss you."

He Loves Me

He loves me. He don't!
He'll have me. He won't!
He would if he could.
But he can't. So he don't.

I Love Coffee

I love coffee,
I love tea,
I love the girls,
And they love me.

Feathered Friends

The Wise Old Owl

A wise old owl sat in an oak.
The more he heard, the less he spoke;
The less he spoke, the more he heard.
Why aren't we all like that wise old bird?

The Duck

Behold the duck.
It does not cluck.
A cluck it lacks.
It quacks.
'Tis especially fond
Of a puddle or pond.
When it dines or sups,
It bottoms up.

The Robin

When up aloft I fly and fly,
I see in pools the shining sky,

And a happy bird
Am I, am I!

The North Wind Doth Blow

The north wind doth blow,
And we shall have snow,
And what will the robin do then,
poor thing?
He'll sit in a barn
And keep himself warm,
And hide his head under his wing.

The Owl

When cats run home and light is come,
　　And the dew is cold upon the ground,
And the far-off stream is dumb,
　　And the whirring sail goes round,
And the whirring sail goes round,
　　Alone and warming his five wits,
The white owl in the belfry sits.

When the merry milkmaids click the latch,
　　And sweetly smells the new-mown hay,
And the rooster sings beneath the thatch,
　　Twice or thrice his roundelay;
Twice or thrice his roundelay;
　　Alone and warming his five wits,
The white owl in the belfry sits.

Counting Rhymes

Three Young Rats

Three young rats with black felt hats,
Three young ducks with white straw flats,
Three young dogs with curling tails,
Three young cats with demi-veils,
Went out to walk with two young pigs
In satin vests and sorrel wigs.
But suddenly it chanced to rain,
And so they all went home again.

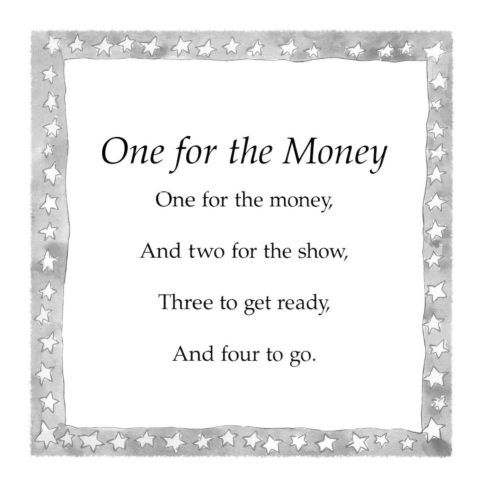

One for the Money

One for the money,

And two for the show,

Three to get ready,

And four to go.

Hot Cross Buns

Hot cross buns! Hot cross buns!
One a penny, two a penny,
Hot cross buns!

If you have no daughters,
Give them to your sons;
One a penny, two a penny,
Hot cross buns!

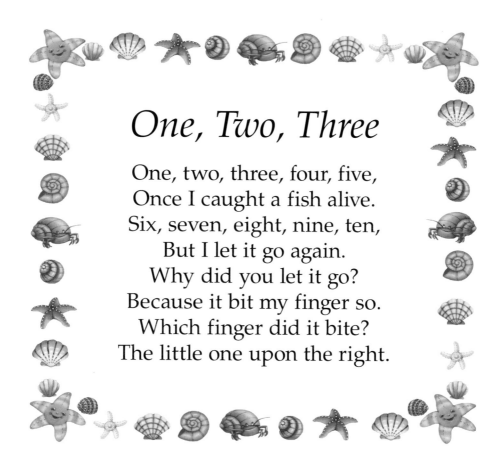

One, Two, Three

One, two, three, four, five,
Once I caught a fish alive.
Six, seven, eight, nine, ten,
But I let it go again.
Why did you let it go?
Because it bit my finger so.
Which finger did it bite?
The little one upon the right.

93

Three Little Kittens

Three little kittens,
They lost their mittens,
And they began to cry,
"Oh, mother dear, we sadly fear
That we have lost our mittens."

"Oh dear, don't fear,
My little kittens.
Come in and have some pie."

Yummy Rhymes

Goober and I

Goober and I were baked in a pie,
And it was wonderful hot.
We had nothing to pay
The baker that day
So we crept out and ran away.

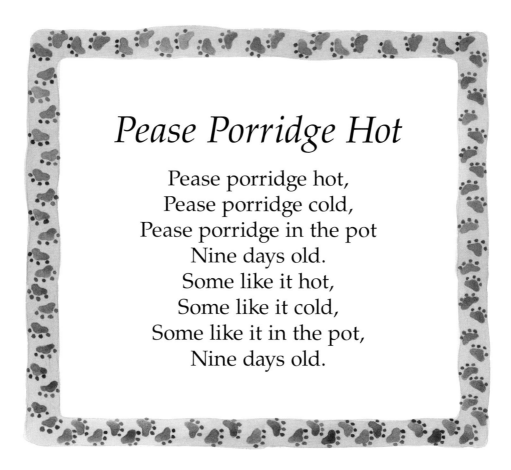

Pease Porridge Hot

Pease porridge hot,
Pease porridge cold,
Pease porridge in the pot
Nine days old.
Some like it hot,
Some like it cold,
Some like it in the pot,
Nine days old.

Little Miss Tucket

Little Miss Tucket
    Sat on a bucket,
Eating some peaches and cream.
    There came a grasshopper
Who tried hard to stop her,
    But she said,
        "Go away, or I'll scream!"

An Apple a Day

An apple a day
Sends the doctor away.

Apple in the morning,
Doctor's warning.

Roast apple at night,
Starves the doctor outright.

Eat an apple going to bed,
Knock the doctor on the head.

Three each day, seven days a week,
Rosy apple, rosy cheek.

Favorite Rhymes

Old King Cole

Old King Cole
Was a merry old soul,
And a merry old soul was he;
He called for his pipe,
And he called for his bowl,
And he called for his fiddlers three.

Sing a Song of Sixpence

Sing a song of sixpence,
A pocket full of rye;
Four-and-twenty blackbirds
Baked in a pie!

When the pie was opened,
The birds began to sing!
Wasn't that a dainty dish
To set before the king?

Peter Pumpkin-Eater

Peter, Peter, pumpkin-eater,
Had a wife and couldn't keep her.
He put her in a pumpkin shell,
And there he kept her very well.

Old Mother Hubbard

Old Mother Hubbard
Went to the cupboard
To give her poor dog a bone.

When she got there,
The cupboard was bare,
And so her poor dog had none.

Old Mother Goose

Old Mother Goose,
When she wanted to wander,
Would ride through the air
On a very fine gander.

There Was an Old Woman

There was an old woman
Who lived in a shoe.
She had so many children,
She didn't know what to do.
She gave them some broth
Without any bread.
She kissed them all sweetly
And sent them to bed.

Jack Sprat

Jack Sprat could eat no fat.

His wife could eat no lean.

And so between them both, you see,

They licked the platter clean.

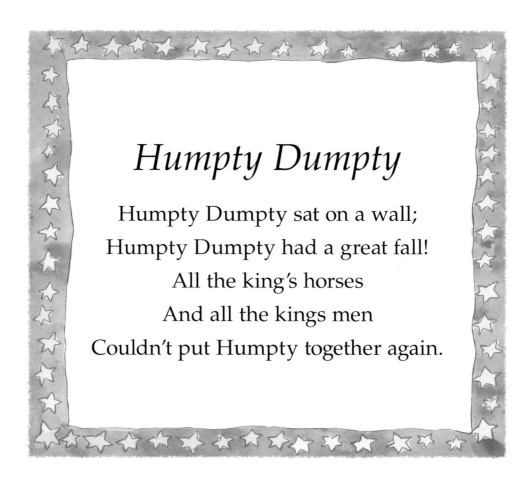

Humpty Dumpty

Humpty Dumpty sat on a wall;
Humpty Dumpty had a great fall!
All the king's horses
And all the kings men
Couldn't put Humpty together again.

Little Bo-Peep

Little Bo-Peep has lost her sheep,
And can't tell where to find them.
Leave them alone,
And they'll come home,
Wagging their tails behind them.

Little Boy Blue

Little Boy Blue,
Come blow your horn.
The sheep's in the meadow,
The cow's in the corn.

Where's the little boy
Who looks after the sheep?
He's under the haystack
Fast asleep.

A Week of Birthdays

Monday's child is fair of face,
Tuesday's child is full of grace,
Wednesday's child is full of woe,
Thursday's child has far to go,
Friday's child is loving and giving,
Saturday's child works hard for its living,
But the child born on the Sabbath day,
Is bonny and blithe, and good and gay.

Puppy Tales

Hark, Hark

Hark, hark, the dogs do bark!
Beggars are coming to town.
Some in jags, and some in rags,
And some in velvet gown.

Where Has My Little Dog Gone?

Oh, where, oh, where
has my little dog gone?
Oh, where, oh, where can he be?
With his ears cut short
and his tail cut long,
Oh, where, oh, where can he be?

What Are Little Boys Made Of?

What are little boys made of, made of?
What are little boys made of?
Snips and snails and puppy-dog tails;
That's what little boys are made of.

What are little girls made of, made of?
What are little girls made of?
Sugar and spice, and all things nice,
That's what little girls are made of.

I'm Just a Little Puppy

I'm just a little puppy
And as good as can be,
And why they call me naughty
I'm sure I cannot see.
I've only carried off one shoe
And torn the baby's hat,
And chased the ducks,
And spilled the milk—
There's nothing bad in that!

Kitten Yarns

Pussycat, Pussycat

Pussycat, Pussycat, where have you been?
I've been to London to visit the queen.
Pussycat, Pussycat, what did you do there?
I frightened a little mouse under her chair.

The Kilkenny Cats

There once were two cats of Kilkenny;
Each thought there was one cat too many;
So they fought and they fit,
And they scratched and they bit,
Till, excepting their nails
And the tips of their tails,
Instead of two cats, there weren't any.

The Cat and the Fiddle

Hey, diddle, diddle,
The cat and the fiddle,
The cow jumped
Over the moon.
The little dog laughed
To see such sport,
And the dish ran away
With the spoon.

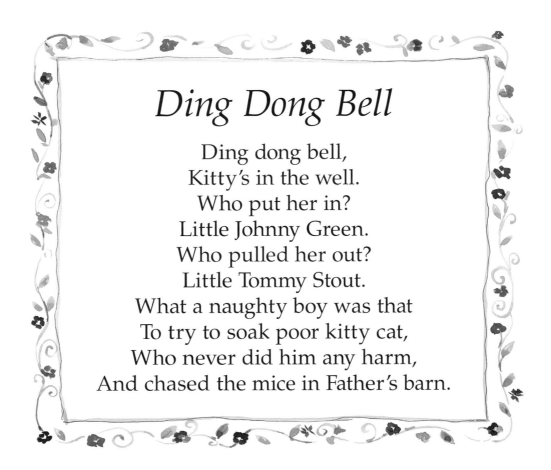

Ding Dong Bell

Ding dong bell,
Kitty's in the well.
Who put her in?
Little Johnny Green.
Who pulled her out?
Little Tommy Stout.
What a naughty boy was that
To try to soak poor kitty cat,
Who never did him any harm,
And chased the mice in Father's barn.

Bedtime Rhymes

Twinkle, Twinkle, Little Star

Twinkle, twinkle, little star,
How I wonder what you are.
Up above the world so high,
Like a diamond in the sky.
Twinkle, twinkle, little star,
How I wonder what you are!

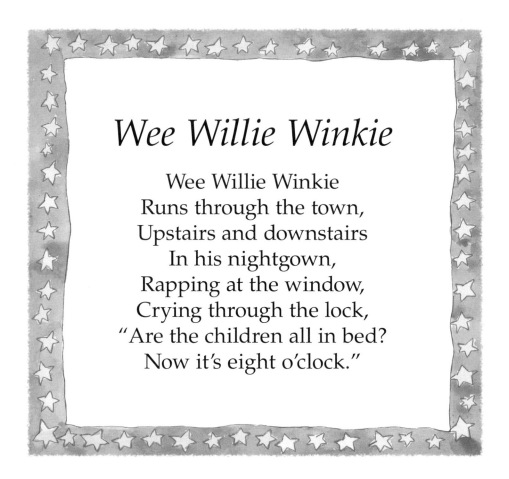

Wee Willie Winkie

Wee Willie Winkie
Runs through the town,
Upstairs and downstairs
In his nightgown,
Rapping at the window,
Crying through the lock,
"Are the children all in bed?
Now it's eight o'clock."

Sleep, Baby, Sleep

Sleep, baby, sleep.
Your father guards the sheep.
Your mother shakes
The dreamland tree,
And from it fall
Sweet dreams for thee.
Sleep, baby, sleep.

Rock-a-Bye, Baby

Rock-a-bye, baby,
On the treetop.
When the wind blows,
The cradle will rock.
When the bough breaks,
The cradle will fall.
Down will come baby,
Cradle and all.

Diddle, Diddle, Dumpling

Diddle, diddle, dumpling,
My son John
Went to bed with his trousers on;
One shoe off, and one shoe on,
Diddle, diddle, dumpling,
My son John.

Sleep Tight

Good night,
Sleep tight,
Don't let the bedbugs bite.

The Cock Crows

The cock crows in the morn
To tell us to rise,
And he that lies late
Will never be wise:
For early to bed
And early to rise
Is the way to be healthy
And wealthy and wise.

The Moon

The moon has a face like a clock in the hall;
She shines on thieves on the garden wall,
On streets and fields and harbor quays,
And birdies asleep in the forks of the trees.

The squalling cat and the squeaking mouse,
The howling dog by the door of the house,
The bat that lies in bed at noon,
All love to be out by the light of the moon.

Come, Let's to Bed

Come, let's to bed, says Sleepyhead.
Sit up awhile, says Slow.
Hang on the pot, says Greedy-gut,
We'll sup before we go.

To bed, to bed, cried Sleepyhead,
But all the rest said no!
It's morning now; you must milk the cow,
And tomorrow to bed we go.

Lullaby and Good Night

Lullaby and good night,
Put your head down and sleep tight.
Lie down now and rest;
May your slumber be blessed.

Index